A Gift For:

_____

From:

_____

Copyright © 2010 Hallmark Licensing, Inc.

Published by Hallmark Books,
a division of Hallmark Cards, Inc.,
Kansas City, MO 64141
Visit us on the Web at www.Hallmark.com.

Editor: Megan Langford
Art Director: Kevin Swanson
Production Artist: Dan Horton

ISBN: 978-1-59530-299-1

BOK1156

Printed and bound in China
JAN11

GIFT BOOKS

All About Dad & Me

The Story of Us... to Write Together

By Laura VanZee Taylor

Illustrated by Rie Egawa-Zbryk

To You & Your Dad,

This book *is* all about you and your dad. It's a fill-in-the-blanks, draw-and-doodle, write-all-over book to complete together. It will help you share tons of fun stuff about you and help you learn a whole lot more about your dad. The two of you have a story to tell, whether you know it or not.

Filling out this book makes a great project for a rainy day or a quiet afternoon—whenever you have some time together. Complete it from start to finish or a little bit at a time. Whatever you like! You'll be sure to find something that makes you smile—and you'll end up with an all-about-Dad-and-me book to keep forever!

And no matter what, don't forget to have fun!

About Us

Full name: _____

Nicknames Dad calls me: _____

I was born on_____
(month)   (day)   (year)

That makes me_____years old.

My hair is_____

My eyes are _____

I am _____ tall and weigh _____

My best feature is _____

The Basics

Dad's full name: _____

Nicknames I call Dad: _____

Dad was born on _____
                  (month)   (day)   (year)

That makes him _____ years old.

Dad's hair is_____

Dad's eyes are_____

He is_____ tall and weighs_____

His best feature is _____

Dad's Portrait
by ME

Portraits

My Portrait
by DAD

Our Family

Who are the people you live with? _____

_____

Do you live with any pets? _____

What are their names? _____

Dad thinks our family is:
- ☐ silly
- ☐ fun
- ☐ full of love
- ☐ weird
- ☐ _____

I think our family is:
- ☐ crazy
- ☐ nice
- ☐ fun
- ☐ awesome
- ☐ _____

Here is a picture of our family:

Draw a picture or attach a photo.

When Dad was little, he lived with _____

_____

_____

Here is a picture of Dad
with his family when he was little:

Draw a picture or attach a photo.

Our Family Tree

My great-grandmother

My great-grandfather

My grandmother

My mother

My father

My brothers and sisters

Me

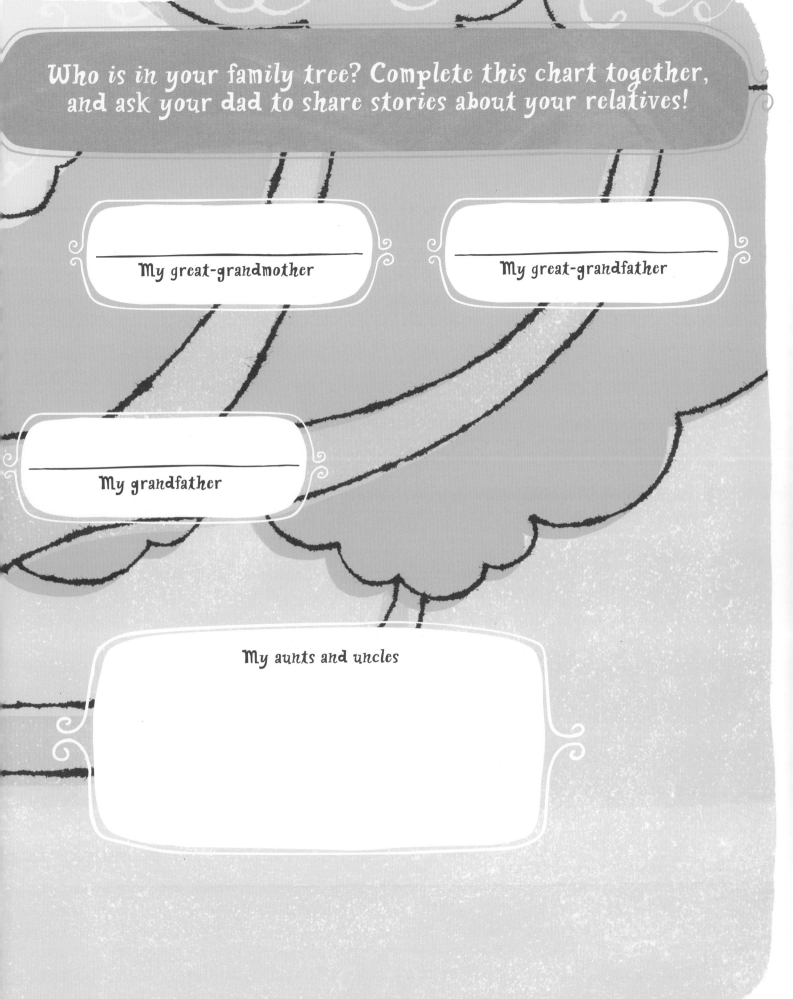

Who is in your family tree? Complete this chart together, and ask your dad to share stories about your relatives!

My great-grandmother

My great-grandfather

My grandfather

My aunts and uncles

When I Grow Up...

When I grow up, I want to be _____

When I grow up, I want to live:
- ☐ in a house
- ☐ in an apartment
- ☐ on a boat
- ☐ in a tent
- ☐ _____

It will be:
- ☐ in a big city
- ☐ in a small town
- ☐ way out in the country
- ☐ in outer space
- ☐ _____

My home will look like this:

When I Was Little...

When Dad was little, he wanted to be _____

When Dad was little, he lived:
- ☐ in a house
- ☐ in an apartment
- ☐ in an R.V.
- ☐ in a tent
- ☐ _____

Dad's home was:
- ☐ in a big city
- ☐ in a small town
- ☐ way out in the country
- ☐ in outer space
- ☐ _____

It looked like this:

Places I've lived:

_____

_____

_____

Places Dad has lived:

_____

_____

_____

Places I'd like to visit:

_____

_____

_____

Places Dad would like to visit:

_____

_____

_____

Draw your favorite place to be together.

Done That

Color in the states you've visited. Use two different colors to compare where you and Dad have been. If you'd like, write in the cities where you've lived and visited.

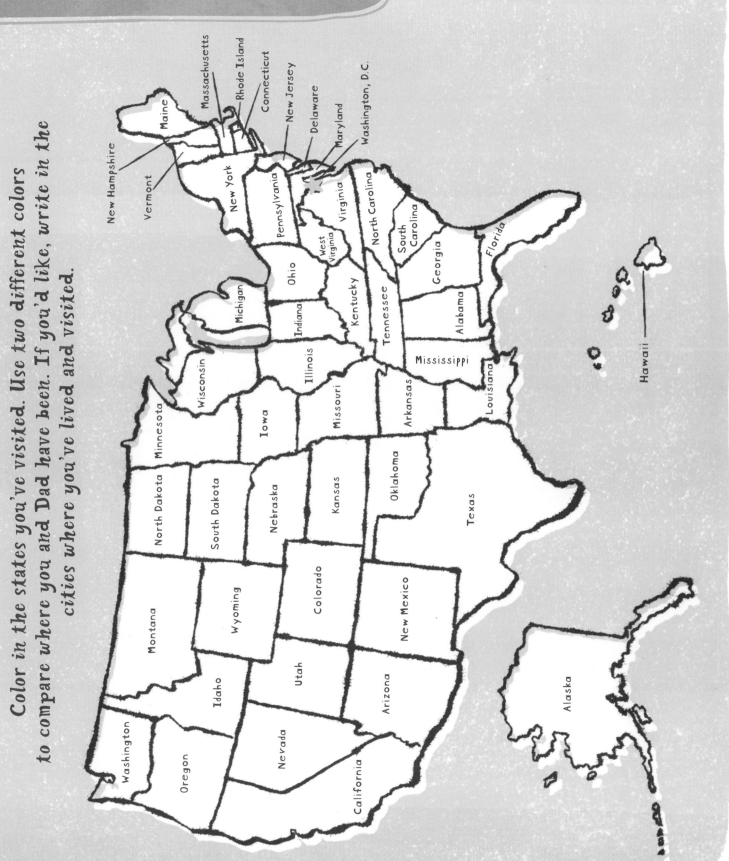

New Hampshire
Vermont
Maine
Massachusetts
Rhode Island
Connecticut
New Jersey
Delaware
Maryland
Washington, D.C.
New York
Pennsylvania
Virginia
North Carolina
South Carolina
Florida
Ohio
West Virginia
Kentucky
Tennessee
Georgia
Alabama
Michigan
Indiana
Illinois
Mississippi
Wisconsin
Missouri
Arkansas
Louisiana
Iowa
Minnesota
North Dakota
South Dakota
Nebraska
Kansas
Oklahoma
Texas
Montana
Wyoming
Colorado
New Mexico
Washington
Idaho
Utah
Arizona
Oregon
Nevada
California
Alaska
Hawaii

If I could do anything I wanted, I would _____

_____

If I were a super-hero, my super-power would be:
- ☐ invisibility
- ☐ super hearing
- ☐ ability to fly
- ☐ super strength
- ☐ X-ray eyes
- ☐ ability to change into any animal or thing
- ☐ _____

If I were President, the first law I would make is_____

_____

If I won the lottery, the first thing I would do is _____

_____

Came True...

When Dad retires, he wants to _____
_____

If Dad were a super-hero, his super-power would be:
- ☐ invisibility
- ☐ super hearing
- ☐ ability to fly
- ☐ super strength
- ☐ X-ray eyes
- ☐ ability to change into any animal or thing
- ☐ _____

If Dad were President, the first law he would make is _____
_____

If Dad won the lottery, the first thing he would do is _____
_____

Our Faves

Dad

Me

Favorite food: _____   _____

Favorite color: _____   _____

Favorite animal: _____   _____

Favorite thing to do: _____   _____

Favorite movie: _____   _____

Favorite TV show: _____   _____

Favorite book: _____   _____

Favorite thing to wear: _____   _____

Favorite sport: _____   _____

Favorite team: _____   _____

Dad   ## Me

Least favorite chore: _____   _____

Least favorite smell: _____   _____

Least favorite day of the week: _____   _____

Least favorite season: _____   _____

Least favorite vegetable: _____   _____

Least favorite subject: _____   _____

Least favorite time of day: _____   _____

Least favorite thing to wear: _____   _____

Least favorite sport: _____   _____

Least favorite color: _____   _____

From the time you wake up until the time you go to sleep...just think of all the awesome things you and Dad could do together! Would you go to a baseball game and then get ice cream? Or would you do something crazy, like travel to the moon or take a submarine to the bottom of the ocean? Write it or draw it. And have fun!

_____

_____

_____

_____

_____

_____

_____

_____

_____

Day with Dad

Take the following quiz, then see how much you and your dad have in common. If you chose different answers, see if you can change each other's mind!

My Quiz
Would you rather...

☐ eat one thing for the rest of your life

☐ never eat the same thing twice

☐ swim with dolphins

☐ soar with eagles

☐ have a lot of money, but be lonely

☐ have no money, but lots of friends

☐ stay awake for a week straight

☐ sleep for a month

☐ hold a snake

☐ let a tarantula crawl on your arm

☐ give up using the computer for a year

☐ give up watching TV for a year

☐ be a rock star

☐ be a movie star

☐ live at the North Pole

☐ live at the equator

Rather...

Dad's Quiz
Would you rather...

☐ eat one thing for the rest of your life

☐ never eat the same thing twice

☐ swim with dolphins

☐ soar with eagles

☐ have a lot of money, but be lonely

☐ have no money, but lots of friends

☐ stay awake for a week straight

☐ sleep for a month

☐ hold a snake

☐ let a tarantula crawl on your arm

☐ give up using the computer for a year

☐ give up watching TV for a year

☐ be a rock star

☐ be a movie star

☐ live at the North Pole

☐ live at the equator

Dad and I have a lot of fun when we:

_____

_____

A few of our favorite games to play are:

_____

_____

Let's play Tic-Tac-Toe!

Dad's Score: _____

My Score: _____

Games

Things I can do:

- [ ] stand on my head
- [ ] whistle
- [ ] talk really fast
- [ ] give excellent hugs
- [ ] sing the entire national anthem
- [ ] win a staring contest
- [ ] eat a cupcake in one bite
- [ ] play an instrument
- [ ] name all the state capitals
- [ ] _____

Things Dad can do:

- [ ] stand on his head
- [ ] whistle
- [ ] talk really fast
- [ ] give excellent hugs
- [ ] sing the entire national anthem
- [ ] win a staring contest
- [ ] eat a cupcake in one bite
- [ ] play an instrument
- [ ] name all the state capitals
- [ ] _____

My super-secret talent is:

_____

Dad's super-secret talent is:

_____

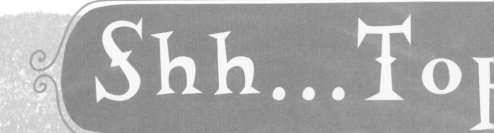
Something Dad probably doesn't know about me:

_____

_____

My most embarrassing moment:

_____

_____

I am usually very brave, but I am scared of:

Secret!

Something I probably don't know about Dad:

_____

_____

Dad's most embarrassing moment:

_____

_____

Dad *is* usually very brave, but he *is* scared of:

_____

_____

One thing that only Dad and I know about is:

_____

_____

If we had a secret club, it would be called:

_____

_____

Our secret password would be:

_____

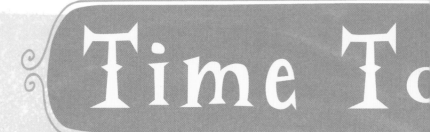

Ask your dad all the things you've always wanted to know about him and record his answers here. Who knows? You may just learn something!

What makes you the happiest?

_____

What's your favorite thing about being a dad?

_____

What do you do when I'm not around?

_____

If you were a cartoon character, who would you be?

_____

What do I do that makes you feel proud?

_____

Did you always know you wanted to be a dad?

_____

What's your favorite flavor of ice cream?

_____

Now write your own questions!

_____

_____

_____

 **Talk!**

Now it's Dad's turn to ask a few questions!

What makes you the happiest?

_____

What makes you sad?

_____

What do you do when I'm not around?

_____

If you were a cartoon character, who would you be?

_____

What do you do that makes you feel proud of yourself?

_____

If you were rich and famous, what would you do?

_____

What's your favorite flavor of ice cream?

_____

Now write your own questions!

_____

_____

_____

Have Dad tell you a funny story. It can be about anything—a story about you when you were little, his most embarrassing moment, or WHATEVER! As Dad talks, illustrate the story here and add captions.

Funny!

Now it's your turn! Tell Dad a funny story (you can even make it up!) and let him be the illustrator.

Describe your dad in three words:

1. _____

2. _____

3. _____

If my dad were an animal, he would be a _____

because _____

_____

Dad always makes me laugh when he:

_____

_____

Some really important things Dad taught me are:

_____

_____

I know Dad loves me when he says:

_____

_____

We Are

Describe me in three words:

1. _____

2. _____

3. _____

If I were a cookie, Dad thinks I would be a _____

because _____

_____

Dad likes it when I help him:

_____

_____

Some really important things I taught Dad are:

_____

_____

Dad loves the way I:

_____

_____

On these pages, attach your favorite photos of you and Dad.
Then write some funny captions together.

Me & Dad

Me & Dad

If you and your dad had fun
filling out this book, we would
love to hear from you.

Please send your comments to:
Hallmark Book Feedback
P.O. Box 419034
Mail Drop 215
Kansas City, MO 64141

Or e-mail us at:
booknotes@hallmark.com